Better Bass With

Rockschool

rockschool

Welcome To Bass Grade 5

Welcome to the Rockschool Bass Grade 5 pack. The book and CD contain everything needed to play bass in this grade. In the book you will find the exam scores in both standard bass notation and TAB. The accompanying CD has full stereo mixes of each tune, backing tracks to play along with for practice, tuning notes and spoken two bar count-ins to each piece. Handy tips on playing the pieces and the marking schemes can be found in the Guru's Guide on page 28. If you have any queries about this or any other Rockschool exam, please call us on **020 8332 6303**, email us at *info@rockschool.co.uk* or visit our website *www.rockschool.co.uk*. Good luck!

Level 2 Requirements for Grades 4 & 5

The nine Rockschool grades are divided into four levels. These levels correspond to the levels of the National Qualifications Framework (NQF). Further details about the NQF can be found at *www.qca.org.uk/NQF*. Details of all Rockschool's accredited qualifications can be found at *www.qca.org.uk/openquals*.

Bass Grade 5 is part of Level 2. This Level is for those of you who are confident in the key skills on the bass and who are stepping up to more advanced skills and stylistic expression.

Grade 4: in this grade you use a range of physical and expressive techniques with confidence, legato and staccato, slides, hammer ons and pull offs, slaps and pulls and accents and you are experimenting with a range of dynamics from very quiet (*pp*) to very loud (*ff*). In this grade you are continuing to develop your ability to play with stylistic authority.

Grade 5: as a player you will be confident in a range of physical and expressive techniques, including the use of double stops. You will be able to demonstrate your abilities across a number of styles and have control over tone and sound adjustments to suit the playing style of your choice. Please note that some of the tunes may now be written out over three pages.

Bass Exams at Grade 5

There are **three** types of exam that can be taken using this pack: a Grade Exam, a Performance Certificate and a Band Exam.

Bass Grade 5 Exam: this is for players who want to develop performance and technical skills

Players wishing to enter for a Bass Grade 5 exam need to prepare **three** pieces of which **one** may be a free choice piece chosen from outside the printed repertoire. In addition you must prepare the technical exercises in the book, undertake either a sight reading test or an improvisation & interpretation test, take an ear test and answer general musicianship questions. Samples of these tests are printed in the book along with audio examples on the CD.

Bass Grade 5 Performance Certificate: this is for players who want to focus on performing in a range of styles

To enter for your Bass Grade 5 Performance Certificate you play pieces only. You can choose any **five** of the six tunes printed in this book, or you can choose to bring in up to **two** free choice pieces as long as they meet the standards set out by Rockschool. Free choice piece checklists for all grades can be found on the Rockschool website: *www.rockschool.co.uk*.

Level 2 Band Exam in Guitar, Bass and Drums: this is for players who want to play in a band

The Level 2 band exam is for all of you who would like to play the repertoire at Grade 5 as a three piece band, consisting of guitar, bass and drums. You play together in the exam, using the parts printed in the Grade 5 Guitar, Bass and Drum books. Like the Bass Grade 5 Performance Certificate, you play any **five** of the six printed tunes, or you can include up to **two** free choice pieces as long as they meet the standards set out by Rockschool. If you take this exam you will be marked as a unit with each player expected to contribute equally to the overall performance of each piece played.

Bass Notation Explained

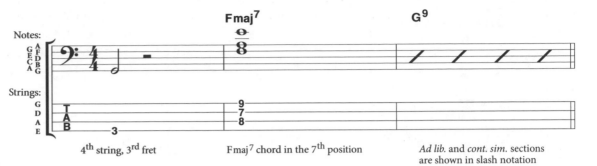

THE MUSICAL STAVE shows pitches and rhythms and is divided by lines into bars. Pitches are named after the first seven letters of the alphabet.

TABLATURE graphically represents the bass guitar fingerboard. Each horizontal line represents a string, and each number represents a fret.

4th string, 3rd fret

Fmaj7 chord in the 7th position

Ad lib. and *cont. sim.* sections are shown in slash notation

Definitions For Special Bass Guitar Notation

HAMMER ON: Pick the lower note, then sound the higher note by fretting it without picking.

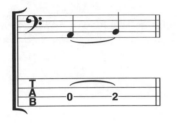

PULL OFF: Pick the higher note then sound the lower note by lifting the finger without picking.

SLIDE: Pick the first note, then slide to the next with the same finger.

GLISSANDO: Pick the note and slide along the string in the direction indicated.

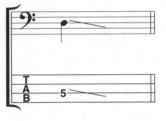

SLAP STYLE: Slap bass technique is indicated through the letters T (thumb) and P (pull).

TAPPING: Sound note by tapping the string – circles denote a picking hand tap, squares a fretting hand tap.

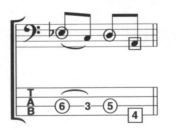

DEAD (GHOST) NOTES: Pick the string while the note is muted with the fretting hand.

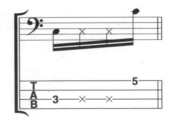

NATURAL HARMONICS: Lightly touch the string above the indicated fret then pick to sound a harmonic.

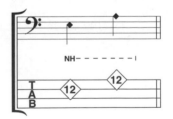

(accent) • Accentuate note (play it louder).

(accent) • Accentuate note with great intensity.

(staccato) • Shorten time value of note.

• Fermata (Pause)

D.%. al Coda

D.C. al Fine

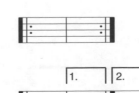

• Go back to the sign (%), then play until the bar marked *To Coda* ⊕ then skip to the section marked ⊕ *Coda*.

• Go back to the beginning of the song and play until the bar marked *Fine* (end).

• Repeat bars between signs.

1.   2.

• When a repeated section has different endings, play the first ending only the first time and the second ending only the second time.

Alka Setzer

Simon Troup

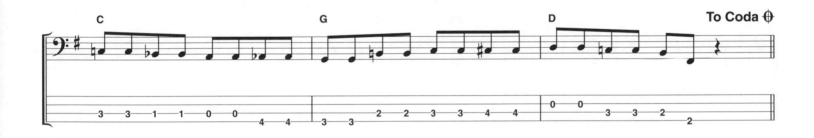

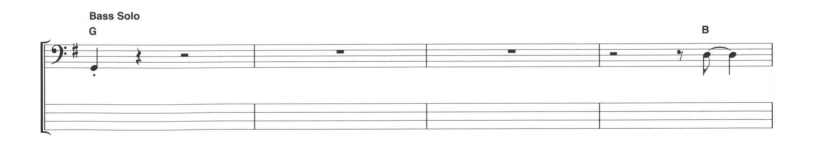

Drum Solo

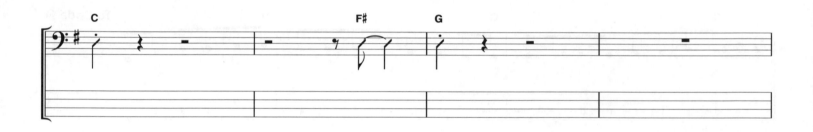

D.C. al Coda
No repeats

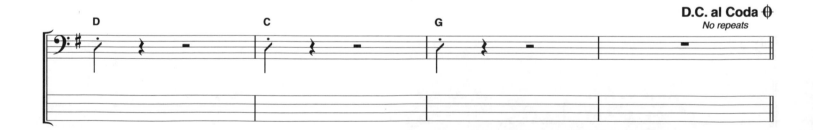

Coda

Sidewinder

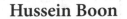

Hussein Boon

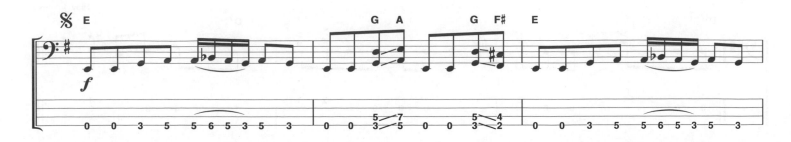

Bass Grade 5

7

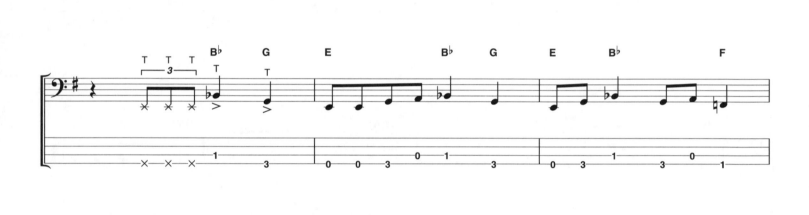

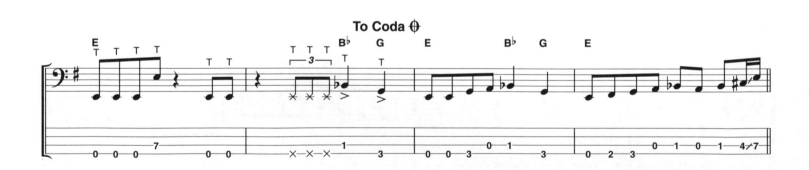

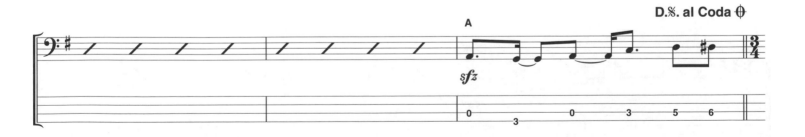

All Funked Up

Jason Woolley

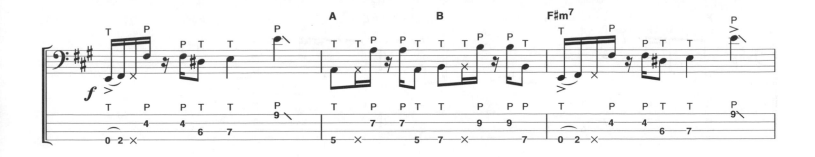

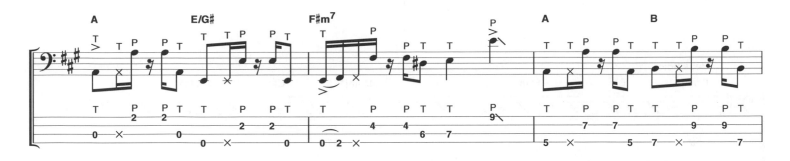

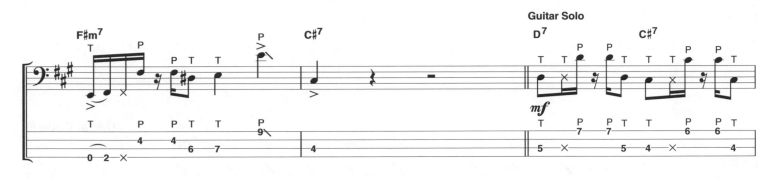

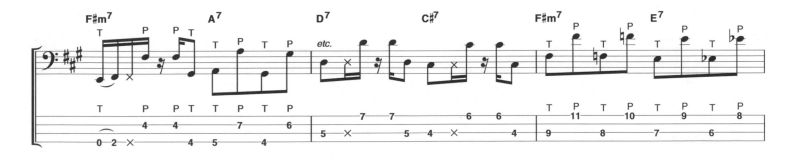

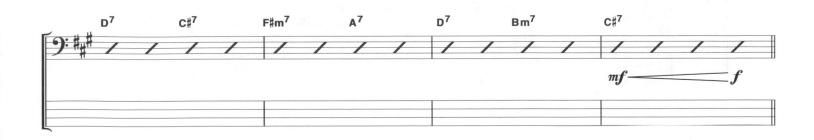

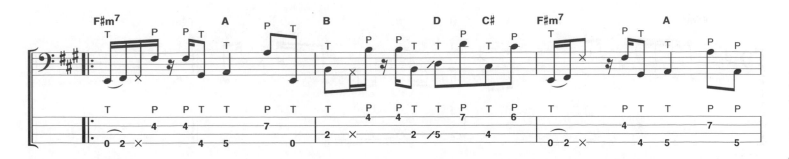

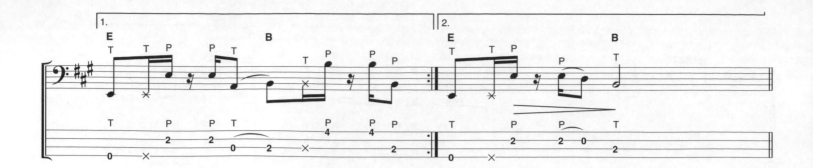

Bass Solo

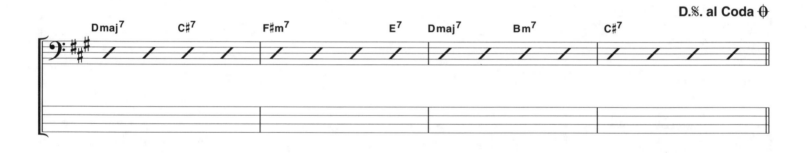

D.℠. al Coda ⊕

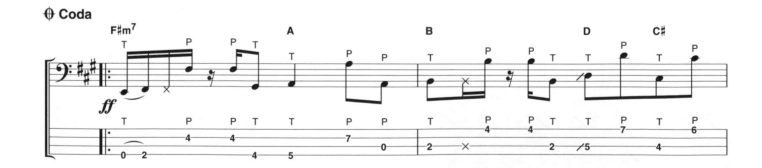

⊕ Coda

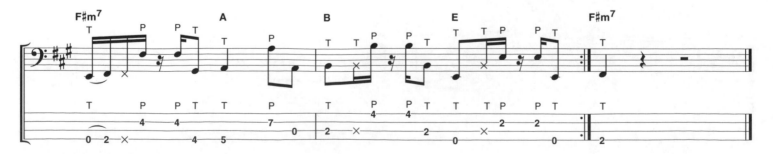

D & A

Noam Lederman

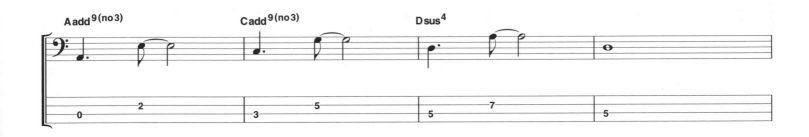

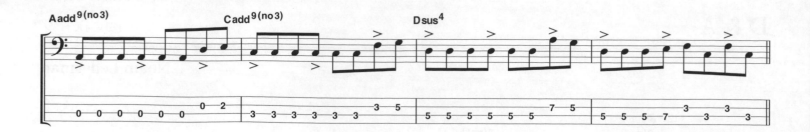

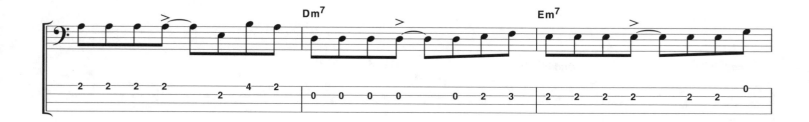

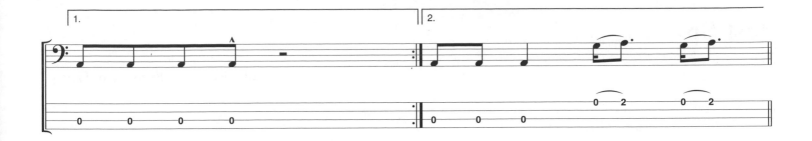

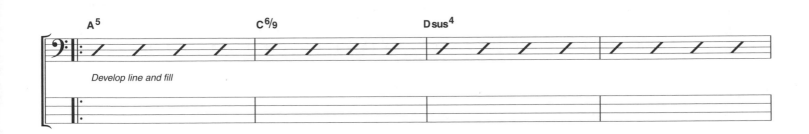

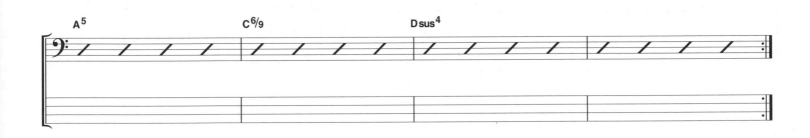

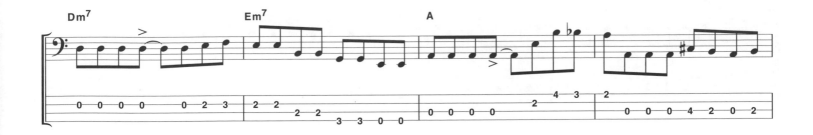

Bust Up

Joe Bennett & Simon Troup

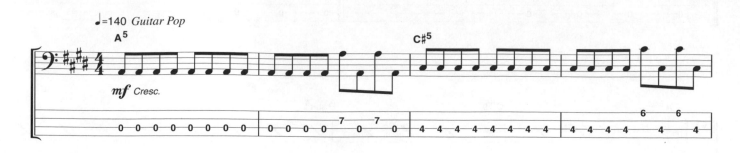

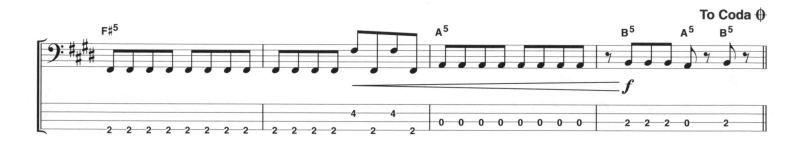

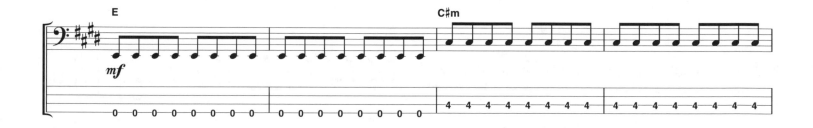

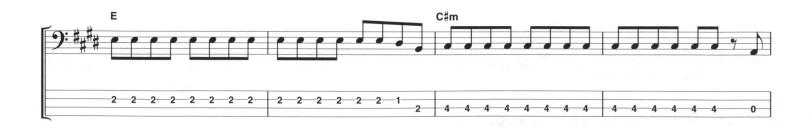

Grade Exam and Performance Certificate Entry Form

Please complete the form below in BLOCK CAPITALS. Information given below will only be used by Rockschool for exam purposes and for Rockschool news. Completed application forms should be sent, along with a cheque made payable to **Rockschool Ltd** for the appropriate fees, to:

Exam Entries, Rockschool, 245 Sandycombe Road, Kew, Richmond, Surrey, TW9 2EW

1. Candidate's Details

Full Name (as it will appear on the certificate):

Date of Birth (DD/MM/YY)*:   Gender (M/F)*:   *This information is compulsory but will be used for statistical purposes only

Address:

Postcode:

Telephone No: Mobile No:

Email address:

☐ (Please tick) **Yes!** I would like to receive all correspondence from Rockschool via email (with the exception of certificates and mark sheets which will be posted). *Rockschool will NOT circulate your email address to any third parties.*

2. Your Examination

Type of Exam (Grade or Performance Certificate):   Grade:

Instrument: *If you are applying for multiple examinations, please continue below:*

Type of Exam:	Instrument:	Grade:
Type of Exam:	Instrument:	Grade:

Period (A/B/C)*:   *Refer to our website for exam periods and closing dates*

Preferred Town for Examination (*Refer to our website for a list of current towns with Rockschool examination centres*):

Rockschool will endeavour to place you at your preferred town, but cannot guarantee this

Please state any dates that are IMPOSSIBLE for you to attend*:

It is not guaranteed that we can avoid these dates

3. Additional information

Drum Candidates. Do you require a left-handed kit?

Will you be bringing your own kit (Grades 6,7,8 only)?   If 'no' Rockschool will provide a drum kit.

Popular Piano Candidates. Will you be bringing your own keyboard?

If 'no', Rockschool can provide either a keyboard or a piano. Please indicate which you prefer :

Special Needs Candidates. Please include a supporting letter with your application explaining your requirements.

All Candidates. If there is any additional information you consider relevant, please attach a note to your application.

4. Fees — *For current exam prices please refer to our website, www.rockschool.co.uk or call us on 020 8332 6303*

Fee enclosed:

Cheque Number: PLEASE WRITE CANDIDATE NAME ON BACK OF CHEQUE

Teacher's Exam Entry Form

Teachers wishing to enter **grade exams** and **performance certificates** on behalf of their students should complete the form below in BLOCK CAPITALS. Information given will only be used by Rockschool for exam purposes and for Rockschool news. You can get up to date information on examination prices from **www.rockschool.co.uk** or by ringing the Rockschool helpline on **020 8332 6303**. Completed application forms should be sent, along with a cheque made payable to **Rockschool Ltd** for the appropriate fees, to:

Exam Entries, Rockschool, 245 Sandycombe Road, Kew, Richmond, Surrey, TW9 2EW

1. Teacher's Details

Title (Mr/Mrs/Ms etc):   Full Name:

Address:

                                          Postcode:

Telephone No: Mobile No:

Email address:

☐ (Please tick) **Yes!** I would like to receive all correspondence from Rockschool via email (with the exception of certificates and mark sheets which will be posted). *Rockschool will NOT circulate your email address to any third parties.*

2. Examination Details and Fees
*For grade exams, please write '**G**' and the grade number in the Grade box (e.g. **G6** for Grade 6). For performance certificates, please write '**PC**' and the grade number in the Grade box (e.g. **PC4** for Performance Certificate Grade 4). †For examination periods refer to our website. Continue on separate sheet if necessary.*

FOR SPECIAL NEEDS CANDIDATES PLEASE ATTACH A SUPPORTING LETTER WITH DETAILS.

Candidate's Name (as it will appear on the certificate)	Date of Birth	Gender (M/F)	Instrument	Grade*	Period†	Fee (£)
1.	DD MM YYYY					
2.	DD MM YYYY					
3.	DD MM YYYY					
4.	DD MM YYYY					
5.	DD MM YYYY					
6.	DD MM YYYY					
7.	DD MM YYYY					
8.	DD MM YYYY					
9.	DD MM YYYY					
10.	DD MM YYYY					
11.	DD MM YYYY					
12.	DD MM YYYY					
				Total fees enclosed £		

Preferred Town for Examination (*Refer to our website for a list of current towns with Rockschool examination centres**):

*Rockschool will endeavour to place your candidates at your preferred town, but cannot guarantee this

Please list dates your candidate(s) **cannot** attend*:

*It is not guaranteed that we can avoid these dates

Band Exam Entry Form

You can enter for one of the following band exams (1 Guitar player, 1 Bass player, 1 Drummer) using Rockschool materials: * Level One (Grade 3 repertoire) * Level Two (Grade 5 repertoire) *Level Three (Grade 8 repertoire) Please complete the form below in BLOCK CAPITALS. Information given will only be used by Rockschool for exam purposes and for Rockschool news. Completed application forms should be sent, along with a cheque made payable to **Rockschool Ltd** for the appropriate fees, to:

Exam Entries, Rockschool, 245 Sandycombe Road, Kew, Richmond, Surrey, TW9 2EW

---

1. Band's Details

GUITARIST Full Name (as it will appear on the certificate):

| Date of Birth (DD/MM/YY)*: | Gender (M/F)*: |

BASSIST Full Name (as it will appear on the certificate):

| Date of Birth (DD/MM/YY)*: | Gender (M/F)*: |

DRUMMER Full Name (as it will appear on the certificate):

| Date of Birth (DD/MM/YY)*: | Gender (M/F)*: |

*This information is compulsory but will be used for statistical purposes only

---

2. Band's Main Contact Details

Main Contact's Name:

Address:

Postcode:

| Telephone No: | Mobile No: |

Email address:

☐ (Please tick) **Yes!** I would like to receive all correspondence from Rockschool via email (with the exception of certificates and mark sheets which will be posted). *Rockschool will NOT circulate your email address to any third parties.*

---

3. Your Examination — *If you are applying for multiple exams, please use a separate form for each*

Exam Level (One/Two/Three):

Period (A/B/C)*: *Refer to our website for exam periods and closing dates*

Preferred Town for Examination (*Refer to our website for a list of current towns with Rockschool examination centres*):

Rockschool will endeavour to place you at your preferred town, but cannot guarantee this

Please state any dates that are IMPOSSIBLE for you to attend*:

It is not guaranteed that we can avoid these dates

Additional Information *If there is any additional information you consider relevant (e.g. band members with special needs) please attach a separate sheet explaining your requirements.*

---

4. Fees — *For current exam prices please refer to our website, www.rockschool.co.uk or call us on 020 8332 6303*

Fee enclosed:

| Cheque Number: | PLEASE WRITE CANDIDATES' NAMES ON BACK OF CHEQUE |

rockschool

ROCKSCHOOL HELPLINE: 020 8332 6303
email: info@rockschool.co.uk website: www.rockschool.co.uk

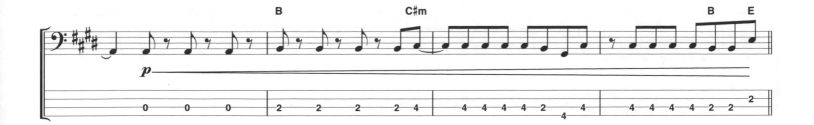

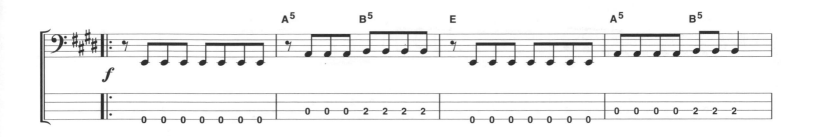

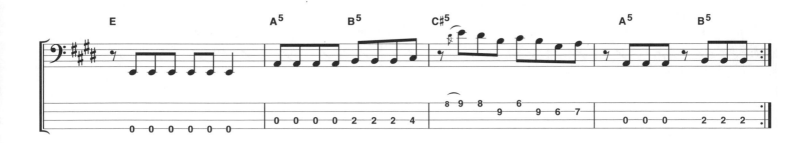

Bass Grade 5

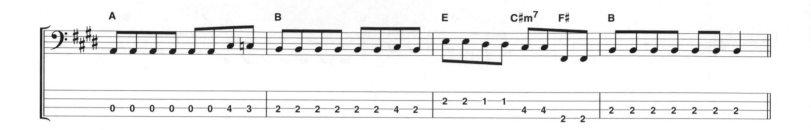

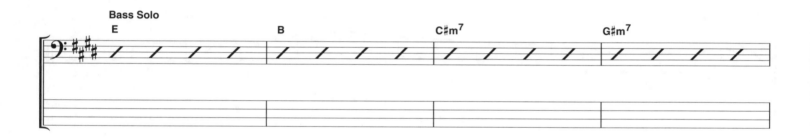

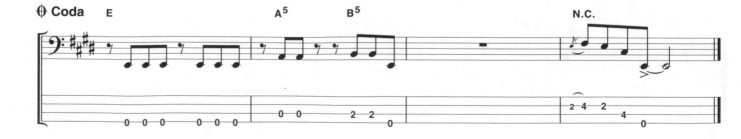

X-Blues III

Deirdre Cartwright

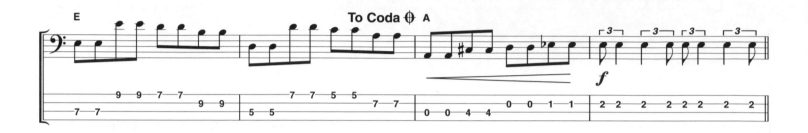

Guitar Solo

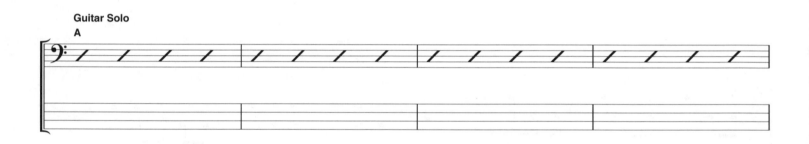

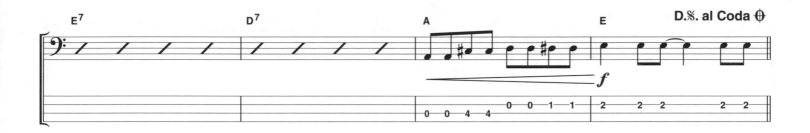

Bass Grade 5

21

Technical Exercises

In this section, the examiner will ask you to play a selection of exercises drawn from each of the three groups shown below. Groups A and B contain examples of the kinds of scales and arpeggios you can use when playing the pieces. In Group C you will be asked to prepare the exercise and play it to the backing track on the CD. You do not need to memorise the exercises (and can use the book in the exam) but the examiner will be looking for the speed of your response. The examiner will also give credit for the level of your musicality.

Groups A and B should be prepared in all of the following keys: D, B♭, F♯, A♭ and C♯, should be played at ♩ = 90. The examiner will give you this tempo in the exam.

Group A: Scales & Modes (all major scales should be prepared slap & muted slap)

1. Major scales. D major scale shown

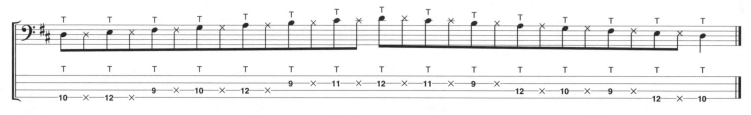

2. Minor pentatonic scales. D minor pentatonic scale shown and should be prepared hammer on and pull off

3. Dorian mode. D dorian mode shown

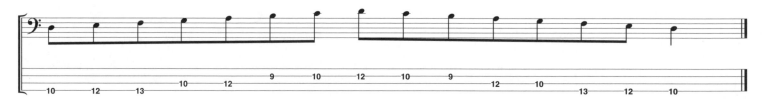

4. Mixolydian mode. D mixolydian mode shown

Group B: Arpeggios (all major arpeggios to be prepared pop and muted pop as shown)

1. Major arpeggios. D major arpeggio shown

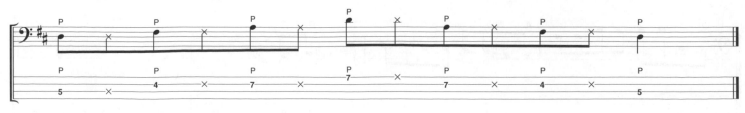

2. Major ⁷ arpeggios. D major ⁷ arpeggio shown

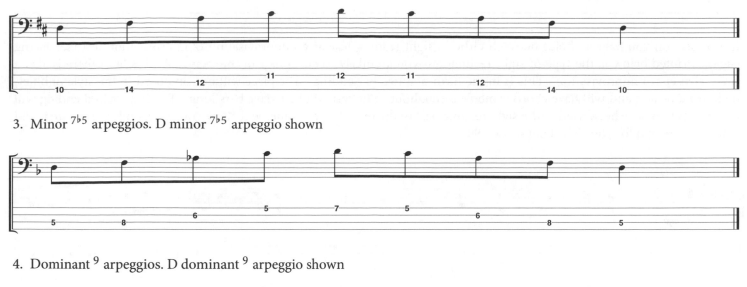

3. Minor ^{7♭5} arpeggios. D minor ^{7♭5} arpeggio shown

4. Dominant ⁹ arpeggios. D dominant ⁹ arpeggio shown

5. Diminished ⁷ arpeggios. D diminished ⁷ arpeggio shown

Group C: Bassline

Prepare the following bassline in the key shown. You will perform this exercise in the exam to the backing track on the CD. The riff shown in bar 1 should be played in the same shape in subsequent bars as indicated. The root note of the riff is shown in each bar.

Sight Reading

In this section you have a choice between **either** a sight reading test **or** an improvisation & interpretation test (see facing page). Printed below is the type of sight reading test you are likely to encounter in the exam. At this level there is also a small element of improvisation. This is in the form of a two bar ending. The piece will be composed in the style of blues, rock, funk or jazz and will have chord symbols throughout. The test will be twelve bars long. The improvised ending will use chords that have been used in the sight reading part of the test. The examiner will allow you 90 seconds to prepare it and will set the tempo for you. The tempo is ♩ = 90.

Improvisation & Interpretation

Printed below is an example of the type of improvisation & interpretation test you are likely to encounter in the exam. At this level there is also a small element of sight reading. This takes the form of a two bar bassline at the beginning of the test. You will be asked to play the bass line in the given rhythm to a backing track lasting twelve bars in the style of rock, blues, funk or jazz played by the examiner on CD. You will be allowed 30 seconds to prepare and the examiner will set the tempo. You will then be allowed to practise through one playing of the test on the CD before playing it a second time for the exam. The test is continuous with a one bar count in at the beginning and after the practice session. The tempo is ♩ = 90.

Ear Tests

There are two ear tests in this grade. The examiner will play each test to you on CD. You will find one example of each type of test you will be given in the exam printed below.

Test 1: Melodic Recall

You will be asked to play back on your bass a four bar melody composed from notes of the F♯ major pentatonic scale. The test will include slapped and popped notes. You will be given the tonic note and told the starting note, and you will hear the test twice with a drum backing. There will then be a short break for you to practise the test and then the test will recommence. You will play the melody with the drum backing. This test is continuous. The tempo is ♩=80.

Test 2: Harmonic Recall

You will be asked to play back the root note progression in the given rhythm from the following progression. You will be told the tonic and hear the progression played twice with a drum backing. There will be a short break for you to practise the test and then the test will recommence. You will play the root note progression with the drum backing. This test is continuous. The tempo is ♩=80.

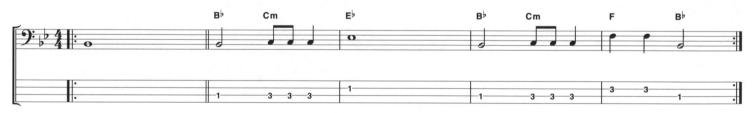

General Musicianship Questions

You will be asked five General Musicianship Questions at the end of the exam. The examiner will ask questions based on pieces you have played in the exam. Some of the theoretical topics can be found in the Technical Exercises.

Topics:

i)   Music theory
ii)   Knowledge of your instrument

The music theory questions will cover the recognition of the following at this grade:

Note pitches	Dynamic markings (*p*, *mp*, *mf*, *f* and *ff*)
Note values	Repeat markings
Rests	Accents, staccato and vibrato
Time Signatures	Hammer on and pull off
Key Signatures	Cresc. and dim.
D.S. and D.C. al Coda	Fermata (pause)
Ral. and Rit.	Slapped and popped notes

Knowledge of the construction of the following arpeggios:

Major	Major ^{7}	Dominant ^{7}
Minor	Minor ^{7}	Minor $^{7\flat5}$

The instrument knowledge questions will cover the following topics at this grade:

Plugging into the amplifier and the bass
Volume and tone adjustments on the bass
Volume and tone adjustments on the amplifier
Two string tuning method as an alternative to an electronic tuner

Knowledge of parts of the bass:

Fretboard, neck, body, tuning pegs, nut, pickups, bridge, pickup selectors, scratchplate and jack socket

Knowledge of main bass makes.

Questions on all these topics will be based on pieces played by you in the exam. Tips on how to approach this part of the exam can be found in the Rockschool Companion Guide and on the Rockschool website: *www.rockschool.co.uk*.

The Guru's Guide To Bass Grade 5

This section contains some handy hints compiled by Rockschool's Bass Guru to help you get the most out of the performance pieces. Do feel free to adapt the tunes to suit your playing style. Remember, these tunes are your chance to show your musical imagination and personality.

The TAB fingerings are suggestions only. Feel free to use different neck positions as they suit you. Please also note that any solos featured in the full mixes are not meant to be indicative of the standard required for the grade.

Bass Grade 5 Tunes

Rockschool tunes help you play the hit tunes you enjoy. The pieces have been written by top pop and rock composers and players according to style specifications drawn up by Rockschool.

The tunes printed here fall into two categories. The first category can be called the 'contemporary mainstream' and features current styles in today's charts. The second category of pieces consists of 'roots styles', those classic grooves and genres which influence every generation of performers.

CD full mix track 1, backing track 8: Alka Setzer

A 70s rock 'n' roll revival song in style of the Stray Cats. The opening section first time round is played softly and palm muted – you may find that a plectrum will help you here and aid you to get a percussive sound. After the repeat, the bass part follows the guitar part. In the break-out section, the bass is the lead instrument for twelve bars followed by the drums. Think of ways in which you can add colour to the part by being sensitive to dynamics.

Composer: Simon Troup.

CD full mix track 2, backing track 9: Sidewinder

This metal song, in the style of Metallica, has plenty of meat for the bass player. The opening sixteen bars act as a counterpoint to the guitar section (note the bars of 3/4 at the end of each of the first three sets of four bars). In the main section the bassline sometimes doubles with the guitar part but as a player you are asked to add your own fills. Expressively, make full use of the accents, slides and the thumbed pedal and ghost notes, as well as the triplet rhythms. There is an eight bar bass solo section before the D.S. al Coda, to be played very loud.

Composer: Hussein Boon.

CD full mix track 3, backing track 10: All Funked Up

This funk tune makes full use of an array of funk bass licks, particularly the thumb slap and pull techniques, ghost notes, slides, slurs and accents. The opening pattern is made up of one funk riff idea that is repeated throughout the piece. It skips several strings and attention should be given to the expressive techniques to make the performance fully convincing. The part should be varied where marked and you should aim to support the solos of the other instruments if you can. There is an eight bar bass solo section marked where you can develop these technical ideas further still.

Composer: Jason Woolley.

CD full mix track 4, backing track 11: D & A

The bass part in this Britpop song opens with an ad libbed accompaniment to the arpeggiated guitar line. When the drums come in this is articulated into a more solid line played at a higher volume. The main groove, however, is made up of accented and syncopated pedal notes played medium loud to start with and then loud, building to a climax, driving the song forward. There is an eight bar solo section before the D.S. al Coda.

Composer: Noam Lederman.

CD full mix track 5, backing track 12: Bust Up

A pop punk song that straddles all aspects of the genre, from Green Day at one end to Avril Lavigne at the other. The bassline begins with pedal eighth notes that drive the song forward, with short eighth note fills to add variety and colour to the part, steadily building in volume; the off-beat eighth notes likewise. The second half of the song continues in the same vein but with a greater degree of freedom and with descending eighth note runs up to the eight bar solo.

Composers: Joe Bennett & Simon Troup.

CD full mix track 6, backing track 13: X-Blues III

A blues shuffle piece that was a favourite in Rockschool's first syllabus. The bassline theme is stated in the first sixteen bars of the song and are varied throughout the rest of the piece with a greater degree of complexity and dynamic colouring. During the guitar solo you should be looking to develop the part further still and really let rip in the twelve bar bass solo. Further dynamic colouring can be used in the D.S. al Coda.

Composer: Deirdre Cartwright.

CD Musicians:

Guitars: Keith Airey; Deirdre Cartwright; Hussein Boon
Bass: Henry Thomas
Drums: Noam Lederman; Peter Huntington
Keyboards and programming: Alastair Gavin

Bass Grade 5 Marking Schemes

The table below shows the marking scheme for the Bass Grade 5 exam.

ELEMENT	PASS	MERIT	DISTINCTION
Piece 1	13 out of 20	15 out of 20	17+ out of 20
Piece 2	13 out of 20	15 out of 20	17+ out of 20
Piece 3	13 out of 20	15 out of 20	17+ out of 20
Technical Exercises	11 out of 15	12–13 out of 15	14+ out of 15
Either Sight Reading *or* Improvisation & Interpretation	6 out of 10	7–8 out of 10	9+ out of 10
Ear Tests	6 out of 10	7–8 out of 10	9+ out of 10
General Musicianship Questions	3 out of 5	4 out of 5	5 out of 5
Total Marks	**Pass: 65%+**	**Merit: 75%+**	**Distinction: 85%+**

The table below shows the markings scheme for the Bass Grade 5 Performance Certificate and the Level 2 Band Exam.

ELEMENT	PASS	MERIT	DISTINCTION
Piece 1	14 out of 20	16 out of 20	18+ out of 20
Piece 2	14 out of 20	16 out of 20	18+ out of 20
Piece 3	14 out of 20	16 out of 20	18+ out of 20
Piece 4	14 out of 20	16 out of 20	18+ out of 20
Piece 5	14 out of 20	16 out of 20	18+ out of 20
Total Marks	**Pass: 70%+**	**Merit: 80%+**	**Distinction: 90%+**

Entering Rockschool Exams

Entering a Rockschool exam is easy. Please read through these instructions carefully before filling in the exam entry form. Information on current exam fees can be obtained from Rockschool by ringing 020 8332 6303 or by logging on to our website *www.rockschool.co.uk*.

• You should enter for your exam when you feel ready.

• You can enter for any one of three examination periods. These are shown below with their closing dates.

PERIOD	DURATION	CLOSING DATE
Period A	1st February to 15th March	1st December
Period B	1st May to 31st July	1st April
Period C	23rd October to 15th December	1st October

These dates will apply from 1st September 2006 until further notice

• Please complete the form giving the information required. Please fill in the type and level of exam, the instrument, along with the period and year. Finally, fill in the fee box with the appropriate amount. You can obtain up to date information on all Rockschool exam fees from the website: *www.rockschool.co.uk*. You should send this form with a cheque or postal order (payable to Rockschool Ltd) to the address shown on the order form. **Please also indicate on the form whether or not you would like to receive notification via email.**

• Applications received after the expiry of the closing date may be accepted subject to the payment of an additional fee.

• When you enter an exam you will receive from Rockschool an acknowledgement letter or email containing a copy of our exam regulations.

• Rockschool will allocate your entry to a centre and you will receive notification of the exam, showing a date, location and time as well as advice of what to bring to the centre. We endeavour to give you four weeks' notice of your exam.

• You should inform Rockschool of any cancellations or alterations to the schedule as soon as you can as it is usually not possible to transfer entries from one centre, or one period, to another without the payment of an additional fee.

• Please bring your music book and CD to the exam. You may not use photocopied music, nor the music used by someone else in another exam. The examiner will sign each book during each examination. You may be barred from taking an exam if you use someone else's music.

• You should aim to arrive for your Grade 5 exam fifteen minutes before the time stated on the schedule.

• Each Grade 5 exam is scheduled to last for 25 minutes. You can use a small proportion of this time to tune up and get ready.

• Two to three weeks after the exam you will receive a copy of the examiner's mark sheet. Every successful player will receive a Rockschool certificate of achievement.